DRUM ALONG

10 FEMALE ROCK SONGS ★ JØRG FABIG

4 NON BLONDES, ANASTACIA, BLONDIE, CYNDI LAUPER and more

WISE PUBLICATIONS
part of The Music Sales Group

London / New York / Paris / Sydney / Copenhagen / Berlin / Madrid / Tokyo

Published by
Wise Publications
14-15 Berners Street, London, W1T 3LJ, UK.

Exclusive distributors:
Music Sales Limited
Distribution Centre, Newmarket Road,
Bury St Edmunds, Suffolk, IP33 3YB, UK.

Music Sales Pty Limited
20 Resolution Drive, Caringbah, NSW 2229, Australia.

Order No. AM999515
ISBN 978-1-84938-391-2
This book © Copyright 2010 Wise Publications,
a division of Music Sales Limited.

Printed in the EU.

www.musicsales.com

PREFACE

Welcome to the newest edition of "Drum Along". If you're not familiar with the first volume, you should carefully read the following pages to understand this method of learning the drums.

The written parts to the songs in this book are devised as lead sheets; you will get to know what this means later on. It is not the idea of this book to transcribe the original drum parts measure by measure and practise them note by note. For this it would need volumes of music and lots of practising time. The method used in this book should help the beginner drummer to play well-known rock songs with simple grooves easily and quickly.

The CD contains recordings of these songs, done with vocals, guitar, bass, keyboard and drums. If possible you should transform these play-alongs into MP3 files using a PC. With an MP3 player on your PC, you can play them in different tempos without changing the pitch. This is important, since you should play the parts very slowly at the beginning and accelerate the tempo later, when you feel comfortable with the song you are working on. Of course there is also a track without drums, so you can play along with the "band".

In this book, you will become familiar with two songs that have a distinct "shuffle-feel". This style of playing is very important in rock and pop music, and should have your undivided attention while practising or listening to the originals. Ask your teacher or an experienced drummer which songs are hallmarks of this style, and listen to as many originals as possible (see end of book).

Enjoy drumming!

EXPLANATION OF THE LEAD SHEETS

Rock songs consist of different parts, which are usually repeated several times during a song. The most important parts are "verse" and "chorus", in addition to "intro", "outro" and instrumental solo parts. "Bridge" is the name for a part which connects to more important parts in which there is a vocal line in the original, an "interlude" divides parts without a vocal line; if there is a very significant instrumental line in an interlude it is called "riff".

For the drummer it is very important to hear the structure of a rock song. Each part is played with a different pattern, for example you change between hi-hat and ride cymbal, or the chorus is played with eight notes on the hi-hat, the bridge with quarter notes. During one part you usually use the same pattern, which can consist of one bar or more. Sometimes one pattern fits a whole song.

The songs in this book are notated as lead sheets. Each part of the song is written in a single line. On the left you have the number of bars, the length of a song part. Usually it is in 4/4 time, if not it is stated on top of the sheet. In the middle of the page there is the name of the song part (verse, chorus, bridge, intro, outro etc.). On the right-hand side you will find the drum pattern to the part. Important: if it is a pattern with more than one bar, you will have to watch the number of repeats. An example: The verse of a song is 16 bars long, you have a four-measure pattern to this part. In this case this pattern needs to be repeated four times.

Sometimes the same part is played with a different pattern, when repeated. In this case the parts are named, e.g. "verse A", "verse B", "verse C". Sometimes you will find "chorus A", then "chorus B", and then again "chorus A". The pattern played with "chorus A" is always the same.

In some parts of a song there may be "stops". This means, that the pattern to this part is repeated a number of times, and then stops on a determined beat. Until the end of the part, there are no drums at all. "Stop in bar 7 on beat 3" means for example you repeat a one-bar pattern six times completely, and in the seventh bar you stop the pattern on beat three, e.g. with a bass drum beat. If this part of the song is eight bars long, the end of bar seven and the whole eighth bar remain without the drums being played.

Sometimes, patterns and song parts have different lengths, for example: the chorus is seven bars long and is accompanied with a two-bar groove – hereby you only play the first bar of the groove and then change to the next song part immediately.

Lots of songs end with "repeat and fade out". Repeat the last pattern of the song as long as you can still hear the other instruments playing and try to play softer and softer as you go along.

All of this sounds very sophisticated, but if you simply read the lead sheets while listening to the music, you will find out that it is quite easy. The song parts of the recordings on the CD are identical to the parts of the original songs. I particularly recommend listening to the original recordings, while reading the lead sheets. This will give you an idea of the style and sound of the original music.

HOW TO PRACTISE

First of all you need to work out all of the patterns that belong to one song very carefully until you are really comfortable with them. During lessons, your teacher could call out the name of a song part while you play, then count one bar, and you change to the new part he called. The next step is to listen to the song while reading the lead sheets and pay attention to the song's structure. Can you recognise the transition of the parts, are there significant guitar lines, is the vocal line going up or down etc.? As soon as you feel comfortable, you should listen to the song once more and mark every new part, e.g. with a crash cymbal on beat 1.

Now you should start to play with the song, beginning slowly. Use an MP3 player on your computer to reduce the tempo without changing the pitch. Count and listen to each part of the song, so you can always play the correct pattern.

Of course the drummers on the original recordings play a lot more than is notated in this book. If you feel comfortable with the song, you can start playing fill-ins at the endings of the different parts, playing variations of the patterns, hi-hat openings etc. Listen carefully to the original recordings and let them inspire you. But never forget, that it is important to keep the tempo and to be sure in which part of the song you are.

This is even more important when playing together with other instrumentalists.

Special suggestions for group education

If your lesson is a group lesson, there are lots of possibilities:

● Drums only: one student starts with a certain pattern, the other listens, calls out a new part, counts to four and takes over, the first one stops, listens and calls out a new part etc.

● With music: one student plays the patterns, the other one marks every new song part with a crash cymbal on beat 1 of the new part.

● The students alternate between the song parts: the first one starts with the first part, the second one takes over with the next etc.

● If there are stops in a song: the first student plays until the first stop, the second takes over, etc.

Remember the following points when rehearsing with a band:

● Always start very slowly.

● Rehearse every part of the song separately.

● Give a lot of attention to the connections of song parts, e.g. play the last four bars of the verse and the first four bars of the following chorus directly afterwards. Repeat this several times.

● Make sure you know which part to rehearse first and don't stop playing if you play a wrong note.

● When you have mastered the song in a slow tempo you can play it a little bit faster.

● Before performing the song on stage you should have plenty of run-throughs. Try and play the song through during rehearsals without stopping, as this is what you will have to do on stage even if you make mistakes!

I'M OUTTA LOVE

Words & Music by Anastacia,
Sam Watters & Louis Biancaniello

ANASTACIA

♩ = 119.5

9 **INTRO 1** *NO DRUMS*

8 **INTRO 2**

17 **VERSE**

STOP IN BAR 17 ON BEAT 1

14 **CHORUS**

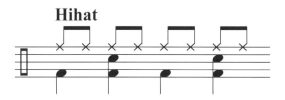

STOP IN BAR 13 ON BEAT 1

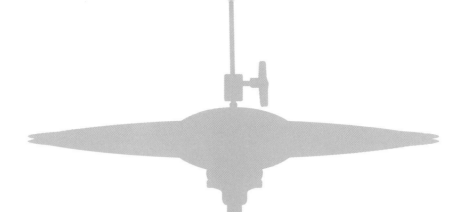

17 **VERSE** *STOP IN BAR 17 ON BEAT 1*

12 **CHORUS**

7 **INTERLUDE**

2 **BRIDGE**

22 **CHORUS** *STOP IN BAR 21 ON BEAT 1*

8 **CHORUS/OUTRO** *REPEAT AND FADE OUT*

Time After Time

Words & Music by Cyndi Lauper &
Robert Hyman

CYNDI LAUPER

♩ = 130

8 INTRO

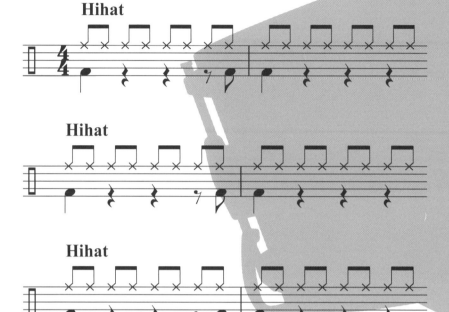

Hihat

8 VERSE A

7 BRIDGE A

8 VERSE A

6 BRIDGE B

Hihat

16 CHORUS

Hihat

8 INTERLUDE 1

Hihat

REPEAT AND FADE OUT

JUST LIKE A PILL

Words & Music by Alecia B. Moore & Dallas Austin

PINK

♩ = 102

4 INTRO A   *NO DRUMS*

8 VERSE A

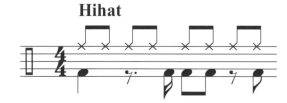

8 VERSE B

8 CHORUS

4 INTERLUDE

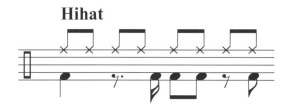

8 VERSE A

8 VERSE B

16   CHORUS

8   BRIDGE

16   CHORUS

8   CHORUS / OUTRO   *REPEAT AND FADE OUT*

7/8

Ironic

Words by Alanis Morissette
Music by Alanis Morissette & Glen Ballard

ALANIS MORISSETTE

♩ = 85

4 **INTRO** *NO DRUMS*

8 **VERSE A** *NO DRUMS*

2 **BRIDGE A** *NO DRUMS*

8 **CHORUS**

8 **VERSE B**

2 **BRIDGE B**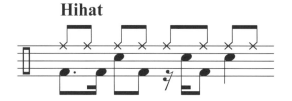

8 **CHORUS**

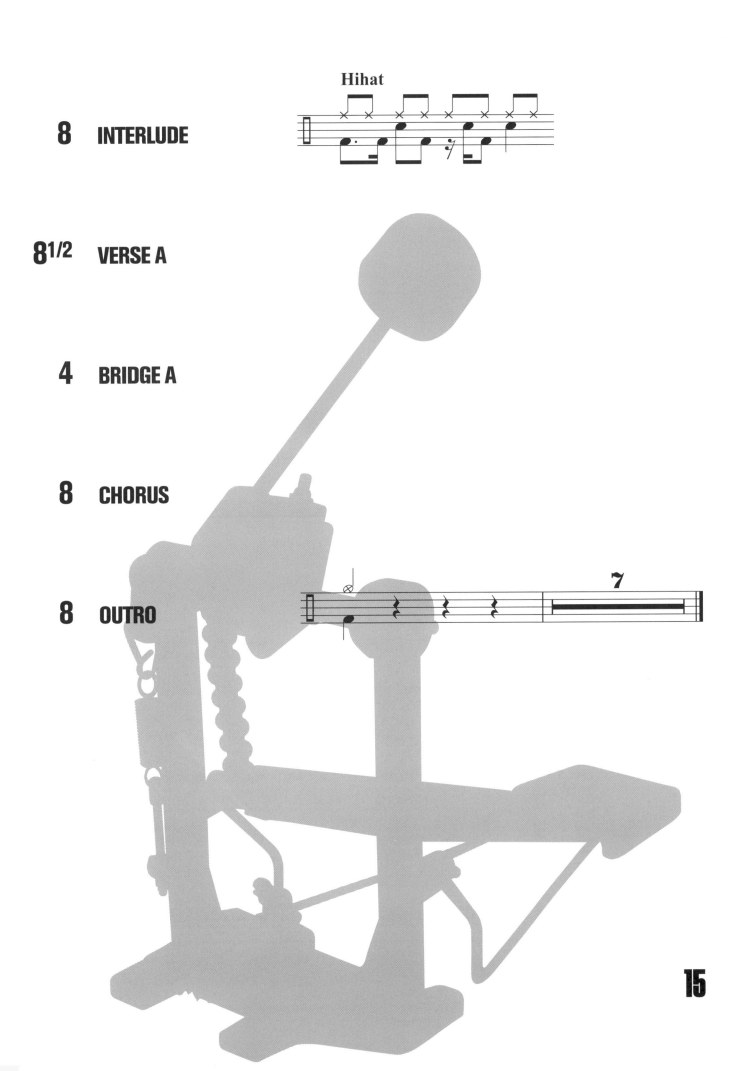

8   **INTERLUDE**

8$^{1/2}$ **VERSE A**

4   **BRIDGE A**

8   **CHORUS**

8   **OUTRO**

Anastacia

4 Non Blondes

B*Witched

Cyndi Lauper

Avril Lavigne

Meredith Brooks

Blondie

Loosavanna

Pink

Alanis Morissette

BLAME IT ON THE WEATHERMAN

B*WITCHED

Words & Music by Martin Brannigan, Ray Hedges,
Tracy Ackerman & Andy Caine

♩ = 90

4   **INTRO**   *NO DRUMS*

8   **VERSE A**   *NO DRUMS*

7   **VERSE B**

9   **BRIDGE 1**

6   **CHORUS**

18

7 **VERSE B**

9 **BRIDGE 1**

6 **CHORUS** *STOP IN BAR 6 ON BEAT 1*

9 **BRIDGE 2**

STOP IN BAR 8 ON BEAT 1

8 **CHORUS** *STOP IN BAR 8 ON BEAT 1*

NOBODY'S HOME

Words & Music by Avril Lavigne, Don Gilmore & Ben Moody

AVRIL LAVIGNE

♩ = 93

4 INTRO

8 VERSE

4 BRIDGE 1

8 CHORUS

8 VERSE

4 BRIDGE 1

8 CHORUS

20

1 **INTERLUDE**

Ride

10 **BRIDGE 2**

Hihat

8 **CHORUS**

8 **OUTRO**

Ride

1 **LAST BAR**

WHat's UP

Words & Music by Linda Perry

4 NON BLONDES

♩ = 66

4   **INTRO 1**   *NO DRUMS*

4   **INTRO 2**

8   **VERSE**

8   **BRIDGE A**

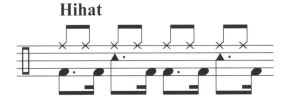

8   **CHORUS**

8   **INTERLUDE A**

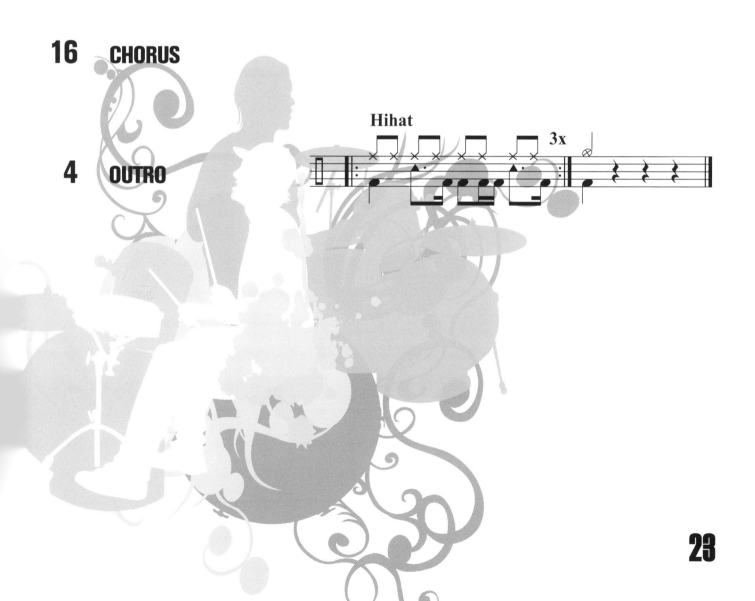

SEE YOU SOON

Words & Music by Marie Frevert, Anke Orschinack,
Katja Panser, Benno Frevert & Elisabeth Schmidt

LOOSAVANNA

♩ = 126

4   **INTRO**   *NO DRUMS*

10   **VERSE A**

8   **VERSE B**

8   **BRIDGE A**

8   **CHORUS A**

8   **VERSE B**

2   **BRIDGE B**

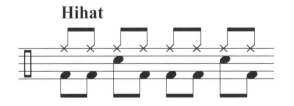

24

8   VERSE B

8   BRIDGE A

16   CHORUS B

3   INTERLUDE

8   CHORUS C

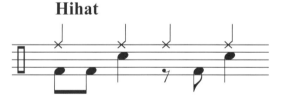

8   CHORUS D

1   LAST BAR

CALL ME

Words & Music by Giorgio Moroder & Deborah Harry

BLONDIE

♩ = 142.5

1   **DRUM PICKUP**

8   **INTRO**
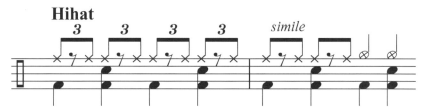

12   **VERSE**

8   **CHORUS**

4   **INTERLUDE**

12   **VERSE**

1   **DRUM BRIDGE**

8   **CHORUS**

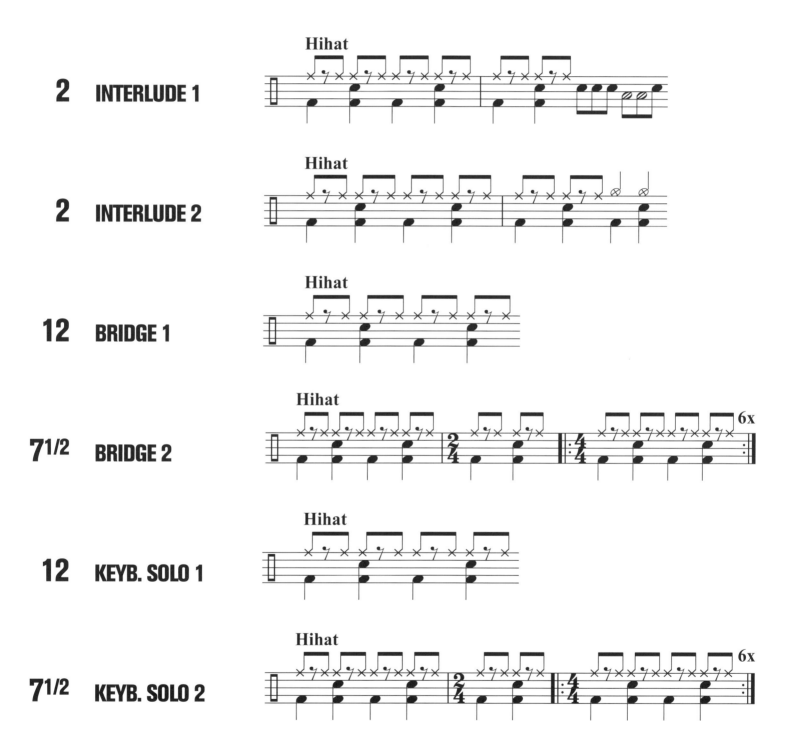

2   **INTERLUDE 1**

2   **INTERLUDE 2**

12   **BRIDGE 1**

7^{1/2}   **BRIDGE 2**

12   **KEYB. SOLO 1**

7^{1/2}   **KEYB. SOLO 2**

8   **CHORUS**   *REPEAT AND FADE OUT*

BITCH

Words & Music by Shelly Peiken & Meredith Brooks

MEREDITH BROOKS

♩ = 96.5
16th Shuffle Feel

2 **INTRO 1** *DRUMS SOLO*

4 **INTRO 2**

4 **VERSE**

3¹ᐟ² **BRIDGE 1**

4 **VERSE**

4 **BRIDGE 1**

8 **CHORUS**

28

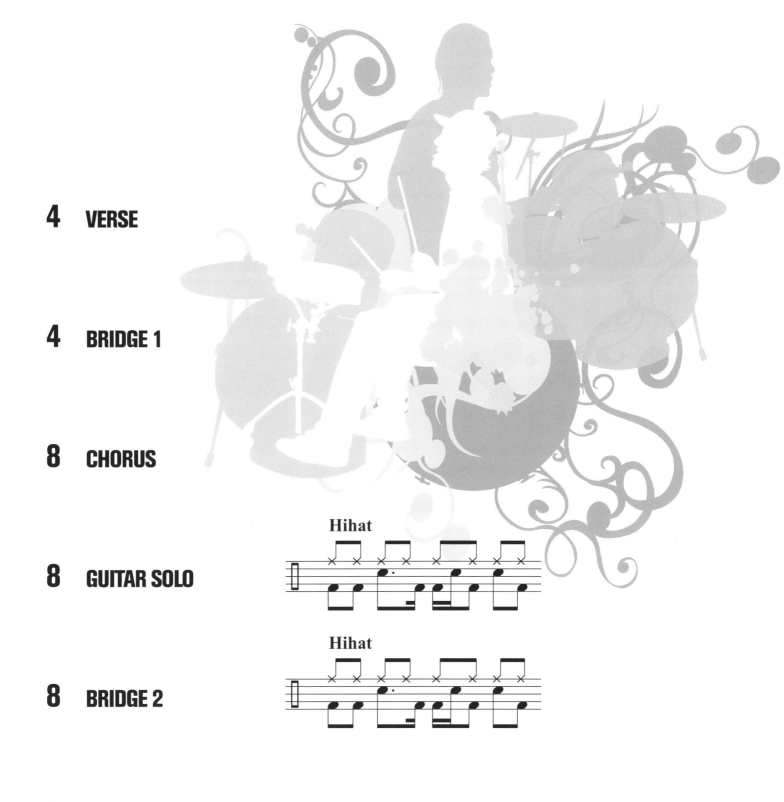

4 VERSE

4 BRIDGE 1

8 CHORUS

8 GUITAR SOLO

8 BRIDGE 2

16 CHORUS

8 OUTRO

REPEAT AND FADE OUT

SOUND AND TIMING – SOME NOTES

I strongly recommend listening to the original recordings. The drummers you're hearing on those tracks play a lot more than is written down in the music, of course. Most of the songs use lots of hi-hat openings, for example. Thereby, the left foot opens the hi-hat on certain beats and thus creates a different sound. Practise these hi-hat openings thoroughly before using them in a musical context.

In some of the songs, the even eighth-pulse of the hi-hat or ride-cymbal is broken by occasional sixteenth-notes. This creates more tension and density, but should also be well practised before using it in a song.

The drummers use fill-ins in many places, especially at transitions into a chorus. Fill-ins are the hallmark of every drummer – I've written out (almost) none so as to give you maximum freedom of choice. Use your creativity here and try out whatever comes to mind in order to find your own sound and style – don't hesitate, and remember: the sky's the limit! New song-parts are then often introduced with a crash-cymbal on the 1st beat.

Generally speaking, you can add lots of dynamics to your playing by using a versatile left foot. When slightly opened, the hi-hat has more drive and volume and can really help to carry a song forward in the bridge or chorus.

"Call Me" is a song with "shuffle-feel", "Bitch" is played in a sixteenth-shuffle. Both are variations on the same generic style, also called "triplet-feel". Hereby, the subdivisions don't consist of eighth- or sixteenth-notes, but of triplets of the same note values, savoured with rests. You can achieve very different effects by playing these more or less "sharply". You should devote lots of time and attention to this musical topic, and not hesitate to ask your teacher or an advanced drummer for advice. Especially the original "Bitch" features all possible variations on the sixteenth-shuffle.

As already mentioned before: listen to the originals and you'll discover many interesting things that are not written in the music. Try to play whatever you recognize and see fit for practising and using in a musical environment. Don't hesitate to ask for help, and what's more – have fun!

SOUND UND TIMING – EINIGE ANMERKUNGEN

Ich möchte dir dringend raten, auch die Originalaufnahmen der Songs anzuhören. Die Drummer spielen hier natürlich viel mehr, als nur das, was in den Leadsheets steht. Bei den meisten Songs wird z. B. viel mit Hihat-openings gearbeitet. Hier kommt der linke Fuß ins Spiel und öffnet an bestimmten Stellen des Taktes die Hihat-Becken, so dass ein anderer Sound entsteht. Übe solche Hihat-openings sorgfältig auf verschiedenen Beats, damit du sicher wirst, bevor du sie im Song einsetzt.

Bei einigen Songs wird auch der gleichmäßige Achtel-Puls in der Hihat oder im Ridebecken durch gelegentliche Sechzehntel aufgebrochen. Das macht das Pattern dichter und abwechslungsreicher, sollte aber ebenfalls gut geübt sein, damit das Timing nicht darunter leidet!

An vielen Stellen setzen die Drummer Fill-ins ein, insbesondere an den Übergängen in den Chorus. Fill-ins machen einen Drummer unverwechselbar. Ich habe (fast) keine ausnotiert, um dir maximale Freiheit zu lassen. Du solltest hier viel ausprobieren, um deinen eigenen Klang und Stil zu finden und zu entwickeln. Neue Songteile werden dann oft mit einem Crashbecken auf Beat 1 eingeleitet.

Generell kann man durch den Einsatz des linken Fußes viel Dynamik in das Spiel bringen. Leicht geöffnet erzeugt die Hihat mehr Druck und Lautstärke, das kann einen Song besonders in der Bridge oder im Chorus nach vorne peitschen.

„Call me" ist ein Song im Shuffle-Feel, „Bitch" wird mit 16tel-Shuffle-Feel gespielt. Das sind beides Varianten der gleichen Stilistik, auch ternäre Spielweisen genannt. Die Subdivisions (Unterteilung des Grundpulses) sind hier nicht mehr Achtel und Sechzehntelnoten, sondern Triolen und Sechzehnteltriolen, unterbrochen durch Pausen. Hier kann man durch unterschiedlich „scharfe" Ausführung sehr starke Wirkungen erzielen. Mit diesem Themenfeld solltest du dich sehr intensiv auseinander setzen und dabei Hilfe von deinem Lehrer oder erfahrenen Drummern, die du kennst, in Anspruch nehmen. Besonders beim Song „Bitch" werden im Original alle Facetten des 16tel-Shuffle ausgelotet!

Wie bereits gesagt: Höre dir die Originale an, dann wirst du vieles entdecken, was die Song auszeichnet und nicht in den Noten steht. Probiere aus, was du davon erkennst und auch selbst üben und umsetzen kannst. Nimm auch Hilfe in Anspruch. Viel Spaß dabei!

EXPLANATION OF NOTATION

 *HI-HAT OR RIDE CYMBAL*

 *SNARE DRUM*

 *BASS DRUM*

 *HIGH TOM-TOM*

 *MID TOM-TOM*

 *LOW TOM-TOM*

 *CRASH CYMBAL*

CD TRACK LISTING

1 **I'M OUTTA LOVE -** FULL VERSION
2 **I'M OUTTA LOVE -** CLICKTRACK
3 **TIME AFTER TIME -** FULL VERSION
4 **TIME AFTER TIME -** CLICKTRACK
5 **JUST LIKE A PILL -** FULL VERSION
6 **JUST LIKE A PILL -** CLICKTRACK
7 **IRONIC -** FULL VERSION
8 **IRONIC -** CLICKTRACK
9 **BLAME IT ON THE WEATHERMAN -** FULL VERSION
10 **BLAME IT ON THE WEATHERMAN -** CLICKTRACK
11 **NOBODY'S HOME -** FULL VERSION
12 **NOBODY'S HOME -** CLICKTRACK
13 **WHAT'S UP -** FULL VERSION
14 **WHAT'S UP -** CLICKTRACK
15 **SEE YOU SOON -** FULL VERSION
16 **SEE YOU SOON -** CLICKTRACK
17 **CALL ME -** FULL VERSION
18 **CALL ME -** CLICKTRACK
19 **BITCH -** FULL VERSION
20 **BITCH -** CLICKTRACK